Q is for

AN ALPHABET

by Mary Elting
& Michael Folsom

Pictures by Jack Kent

Duck
GUESSING GAME

SCHOLASTIC INC.
New York Toronto London Auckland
Sydney New Delhi Hong Kong

P is for Jamie and S is for Raphael

Illustrations were executed in pen and ink and digital media.
Illustrations colorized by Michelle Gengaro-Kokmen.
The text was set in 29-point Miller Text Roman.

ISBN-13: 978-0-545-26501-0
ISBN-10: 0-545-26501-0

10 40 19 18 17 16 15 14

A is for Zoo

TICKETS
ZOO
ENTRANCE

Why?

BEAR
LION
ZOO
25¢

Because . . .

TIGER
MONKEY

Animals live in the Zoo.

B is for Dog

MAIN ST.
SIDE ST.

Why?

BARK
BARK
BARK
BARK
BARK

Because a Dog **B**arks

C is for Hen

Why?

CLUCK,
CLUCK,
CLUCK!

Because a Hen Clucks

D is for Mole

Why?

MOLES WORKING

Because a Mole Digs

E is for Whale
Why?

Because . . .

a Whale is Enormous

F is for Bird

Why?

Because a Bird Flies

G is for Horse

Why?

Because a Horse Gallops

H is for Owl

Why?

HOOT

Because an Owl **H**oots

I is for Mosquito

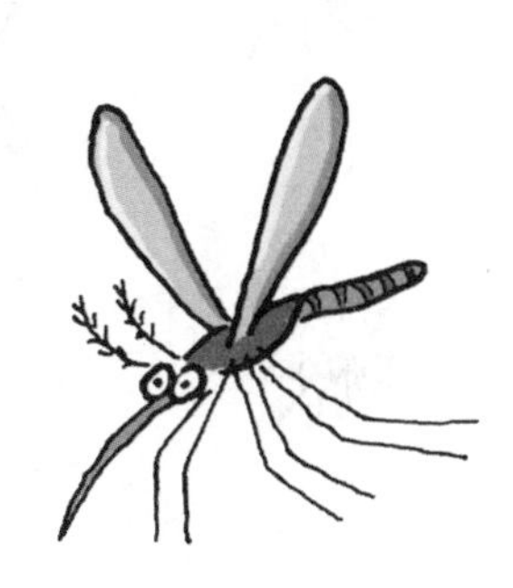

Why?

Because
Mosquito bites Itch

J is for Kangaroo

Why?

Because a Kangaroo Jumps

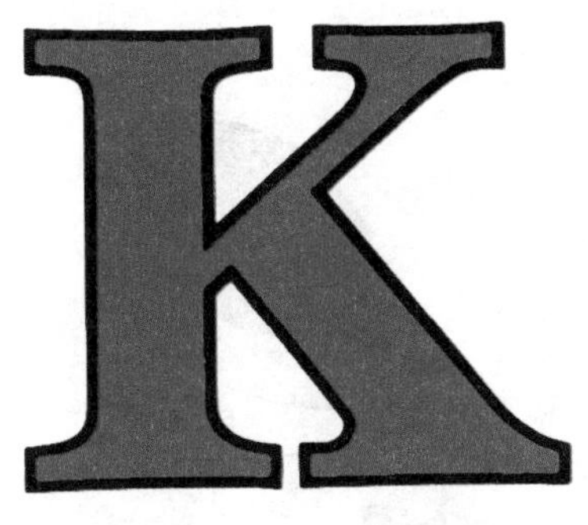 is for Mule

Why?

Because a Mule **K**icks

L is for Frog

Why?

Because a Frog Leaps

M is for Cow

Why?

MOO
MOO
MOO
MOO
MOO
MOO
MOO
MOO

Because a Cow Moos

N is for Cat

Why?

Because a cat **N**aps

O is for Pig
Why?

OINK,
OINK?
OINK,
OINK,
OINK!
OINK

Because a Pig Oinks

P is for Chick

Why?

PEEP
PEEP
PEEP

Because a Chick **P**eeps

Q is for Duck

Why?

TWEET
QUACK
QUACK
QUACK
QUACK

Because a Duck Quacks

R is for Lion

Why?

ROAR

Because a Lion Roars

S is for Camel

Why?

Because a Camel **S**pits

T is for Elephant

Why?

Because
an Elephant **T**rumpets

U is for Prairie Dog

Why?

MAIL

Because Prairie Dogs live

HOME
SWEET
HOME

Underground

V is for Chameleon

Why?

Because a
Chameleon seems to Vanish

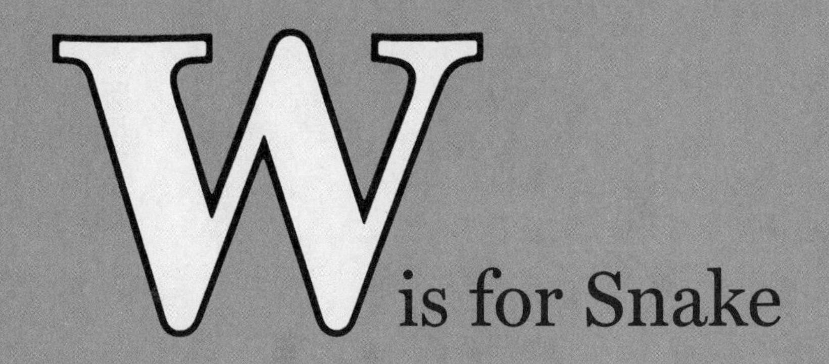

W is for Snake

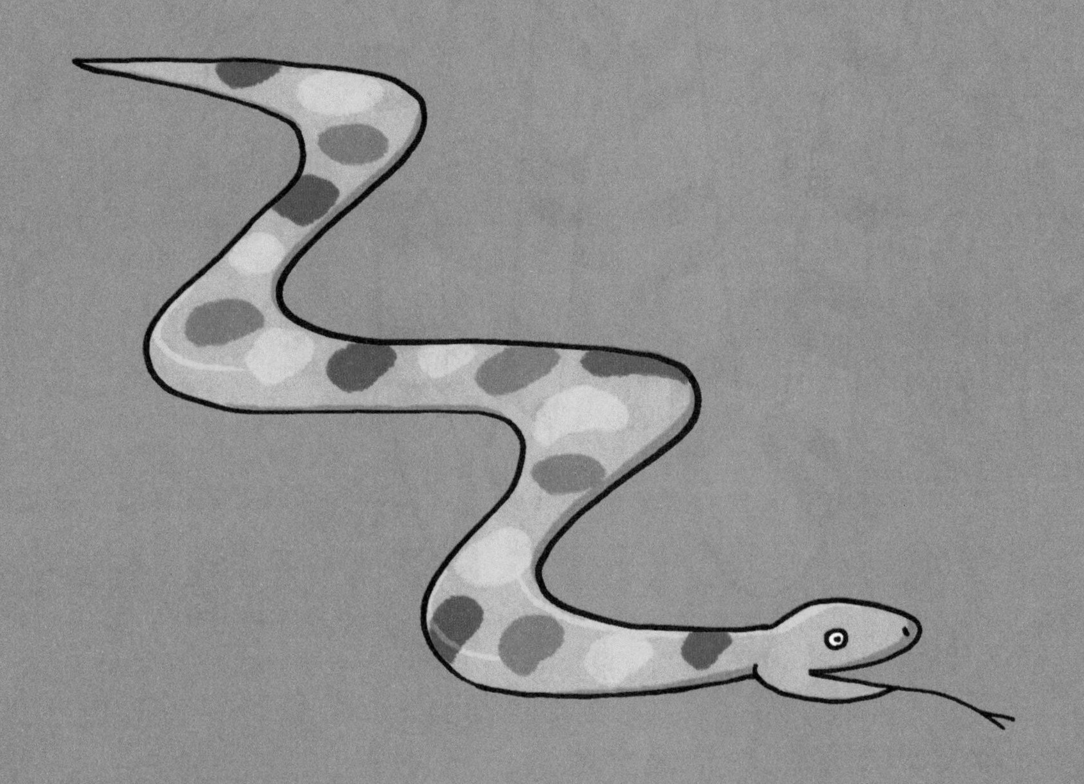

Why?

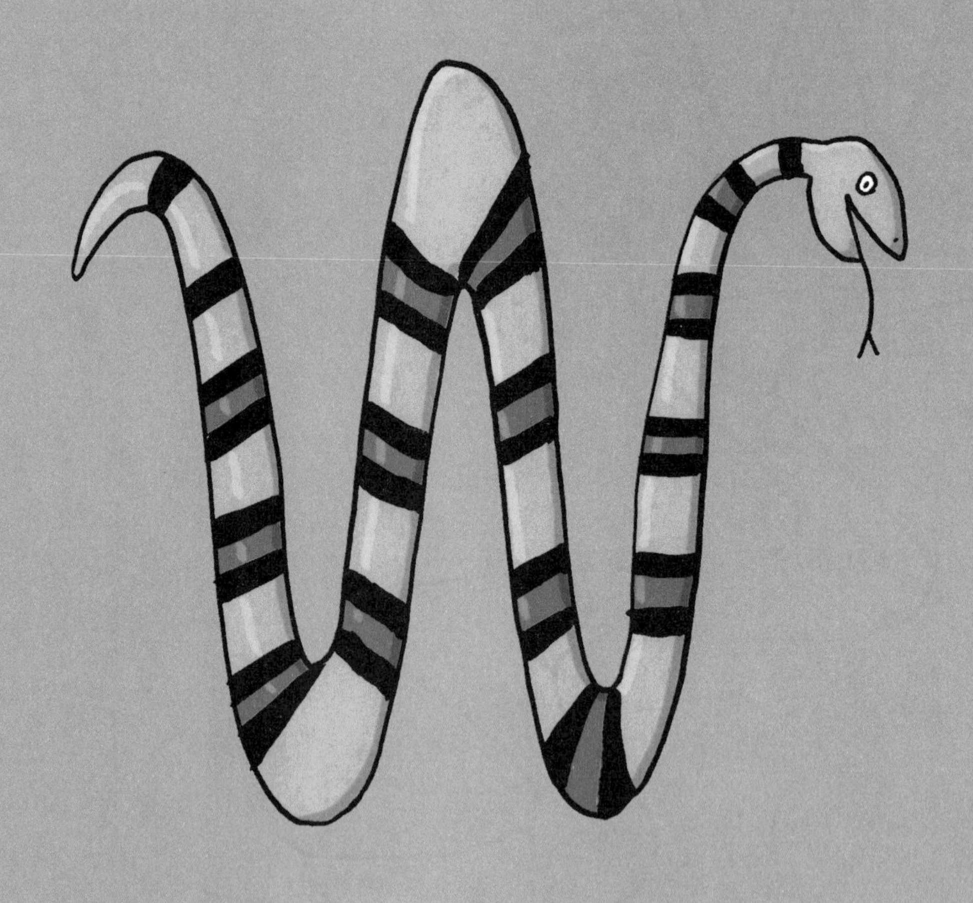

Because a Snake **W**iggles

is for Dinosaur

Why?

Because Dinosaurs are

eXtinct

Y is for Coyote

Why?

Because a Coyote Yowls

Z is for Animals
Why?

ZOO
ZOO
EXIT

Because
Animals live in the Zoo